WRIGLE WRITINGS

Bernard Wrigley

Songs & Monologues

LANDY PUBLISHING 1999

© Copyright 1999 Bernard Wrigley
www.bernardwrigley.com

ISBN 1 872895 49 2

British Library in Catalogue Publication Data
A catalogue record of this book is available from the British Library

Layout and drawings by *Cunsanto Design*, 01204 697926
Printed by Nayler the Printer Ltd., Accrington, 01254 234247

Contents

• •

Introduction

I first started writing songs and monologues in earnest when I joined The Ken Campbell Roadshow in 1970. Before that, as one half of Dave & Bernard, we wrote songs only when a traditional one wouldn't fit the bill. The urban myths that Ken collected together are in fact modern traditional stories - passed on by word of mouth. I got a lot of encouragement from A. L. Lloyd, one of the great figures of the folk revival and Artistic Director for Topic Records at the time. So, special thanks to Bert, the roadshow cast - Ken, Bob, Jane & Dave, and to my sometime co-writers - Dave Dutton, Henry Boot and Dave Roberts, without whom some of these writties would not exist. Here's to the next instalment!

PIE SATURDAY

Roll up, roll up and purchase your pies
They're only tuppence apiece
They're tasty and round, they're wholesome and sound
And they're made of the best Bolton meat

When the crowd starts coming I'll sell 'em so quick
I know I'll be rushed off my feet
So get yours in now while there's some left to sell
They're succulent, tasty and sweet

Roll up, roll up and purchase your pies
They're only three ha'pence apiece
They're tasty and round, they're wholesome and sound
And they're made of the best Bolton meat

I've spent all my money in making my pies
It's cost me a month's rent you see
But wi't'profit I'll make I'll have brandy and cake
Instead of black puddings and tea

Roll up, roll up and purchase your pies
They're only a penny apiece
They're tasty and round, they're wholesome and sound
And they're made of the best Bolton meat

Now that's the last offer I'm making today
They're the cheapest you'll find in the town
They cost me five pound, now look what I've found
They've outnumbered the people in t'ground

Roll up, roll up and purchase your pies
They're only a ha'penny apiece
They're tasty and round, they're wholesome and sound
And they're made of the best Bolton meat

Well that's finished me, I'll have to go home
But I haven't enough money for t'tram
I'm stony broke and I think it's no joke
I'll be borrowing some cash off my mam

Roll up, roll up and take home your pies
I'm giving the buggers away
I've had 'em a week, they're developing feet
They're the fastest in Bolton today

5

OUR BILL & THE CONCRETE MIXER

Our Bill had a concrete mixer
He was coming home last night
When he come down t'street and he saw his house
There's a sports car parked outside

He thought *"Here's me going out to work
And my wife's at home on t'job"*
So he swore he'd get her lover boy
And smack him up his gob

Then he thought *"Now look here Billy lad
Use what's under your crop"*
So he ups with his concrete mixer
- Fills the car right up to t'top

Then he gets back in his cab and sits
As quiet as a mouse
And he sees the bloke coming to his car
But he come from next door's house

Well, Bill starts up his engine
He'd never felt such a prat
He was down that road and a mile away
In twenty seconds flat

But if Bill had stayed a bit longer
He'd have seen his wife, so sweet
Giving a kiss to her lover boy
As he pedalled down the street

So now his missus gets her oats
And Bill, he feels a berk
For thinking his wife was having it off
While he was out at work

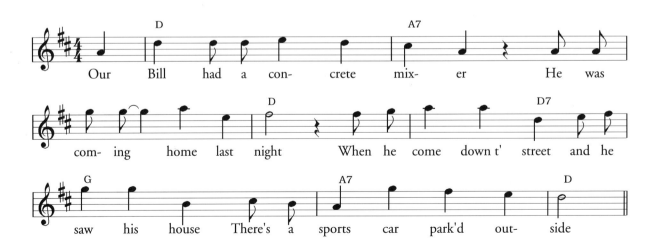

Our Bill had a con- crete mix- er He was com- ing home last night When he come down t' street and he saw his house There's a sports car park'd out- side

6

ELEPHANTITIS

The other day I got up, I'd been suppin' t'night before
My teeth were feeling itchy, my head was feeling sore
I fell outside and caught a bus to t'other side of town
When I passed a restaurant window with a notice upside down

It read *"We serve you anything from egg and chips and beans*
To custard butties, cornflake pies and curried mice in cream
We've buckets full of tripe and stew and plates of jellied eels
And we'll bring them in a wheelbarrow if you want them served on wheels"

I thought *"Ooo, that sounds interesting,"* 'cause I like to vary meals
And I've never eaten cornflake pie, though I've heard of 'eels on wheels'
I thought *"I'll go and have a laugh here, I'll pull 'em down a peg*
And if they bring me what I ask for - I swear to eat my trouser leg"

I went inside, took off my coat and found an empty place
The waiter came up smiling and he looked me in the face
I thought *"When I've finished ordering, pal, you'll wish I'd never come*
I'll have two right-handed parrot beaks and a thick-sliced monkey's bum"

"Righto" he said, and off he went. Before I'd time to blink
He'd brought the lot out on a plate and said *"D'you want a drink?"*
"Aye" I said *"A brandy ... no, you'd better make it two*
If I have to eat my trouser leg I'll be needing quite a few"

I felt a bit defeated but I'd still got some more cash
So I plucked up all my courage, thought I'd have another bash
I called him over, serious like, to show it wasn't fun
"Two elephant goolies on toast" I said, *"Er, medium, not well done"*

He'd been gone about a minute - I thought I had him stuck
When in the road outside there came a sixteen wheeler truck
The waiter jumped down from the cab, opened t'trailer door
And rolled out two of the biggest balls I'd ever seen before

He rolled them in the restaurant as quick as he was able
He had to fix some ramps up to get them on the table
He said *"Sorry I took so long, but t'shops round here's all closed*
You'll have to eat them on their own - we've run clean out of toast"

Well, now I eat my meals at home - I'm a quiet sort of bloke
I never try to argue , I never tell a joke
I never throw my weight round but I take this sound advice
Don't take on people for a lark - 'cause trousers don't taste nice

THE POLICE CONSTABLE & THE RARE BUTTERFLY

Harold Brown was thirty three and worked in Barclay's Bank
You could tell by his pin-striped bowler and his matching tie and hank
He soon would be a manager, so he watched his Qs and P
The sort of bloke a mother likes her daughter to bring to tea

Last night he's coming home from work and crossing near some rubble
When a stabbing pain shot through his guts and creased him over double
He clutched his stomach as he hit the pavement with a crunch
And only wished he hadn't had that curry for his lunch

As the pain went lower, Harold knew what he must do
He'd to use the ground beneath him as he did when on the loo
So he whips down his trousers, his long john trolleybags too
And he moves his legs apart a bit, so's he wouldn't splash his shoe

He squatted down, clenched his teeth, and gave a mighty jerk
He hoped no-one was looking, or he'd feel a proper berk
But as relief came flooding down he heard a pair of feet
And there was PC Bloodstone - our Harold's on his beat

Before the copper reached him, Harold thought in double time
He whipped his bowler off his head to cover up his crime
He tried to hold his trousers up, he whistled as he sat
And he hoped he wouldn't ask him what he kept beneath his hat

"Good evening, lad" the copper says, and he looked where Harold sat
"What makes you squat upon the floor whilst clutching at your hat?"
"Oh, it's funny you should ask" says Harold, sweating on his feet
"I'm a butterfly collector, and I've caught a special treat"

"That's interesting" the copper says, *"I've done a bit myself
And I've even put them in a book and pressed them on the shelf.
What sort is it? ... A brown admiral? ... Now is that like the red?"*
"Er, no, more like the rear" says Harold, wishing he were dead

"Trouble is" our Harold says, *"I haven't brought my net -
I've left it in our house, you see"* but t'policeman says *"Don't fret -
You get the net, I'll hold the hat."* Says Harold *"You're a gent
I'll be back inside a minute"* and no sooner said, he went

For three long hours the copper held the hat - his fingers got quite numb
And since he'd squatted all the time, he'd heelmarks on his bum
But as he pondered whether or not to get back on his beat
He recognized the shuffle of the chief inspector's feet

"Good evening lad" the gaffer says, *"Have your tootsies given out?"*
"Oh, yes sir, no sir" Bloodstone says *"You see, I'm helping out.
The bloke who owns this bowler went to go and get his net
'Cause he's left a butterfly under it ... but he hasn't come back yet"*

"How long has he been gone?" *"About two minutes"* said the lad
And though he smiled up pleasantly, the inspector seemed quite mad
He stooped to have a listen, making sure no-one was coming
"Can you hear it, sir?" the PC says. *"Er, yes ... I think it's humming"*

*"Now this is daft, we're wasting time standing round like this
I'll have to make a grab for it, and it's hard cheese if we miss
You lift the hat up quickly when I've counted up to four
I'll soon have this one cracked - I've handled stiffer ones before"*

The tension mounted as the copper counted one, two, three, then four
The inspector dived and landed in a heap upon the floor
His hands had gone discoloured - he knew it was all a cod
"Did you catch it?" says the PC. *"No, but I've frightened the little sod"*

THE ONE PLACE FOR ME

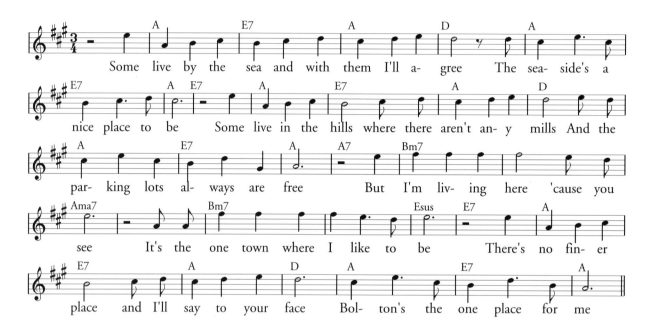

Some live by the sea and with them I'll agree
The seaside's a nice place to be
Some live in the hills where there aren't any mills
And the parking lots always are free
But I'm living here cause you see
It's the one town where I like to be
There's no finer place and I'll say to your face
Bolton's the one place for me

There's houses galore there's pubs by the score
I can say that I know all of them
There's a funny shaped theatre they've built it quite near to
The Town Hall and it looks quite a gem
There's fountains and statues on show
And a precinct where cars mustn't go
I'll tell you again that in spite of the rain
Bolton's the one place for me

Some folk say it's smoky and dirty and poky
And it's nothing but houses and grime
But if they'd come to see then they'd have to agree
It's changing its face all the time
If you don't like the motorways there
Get out and breathe fresh moorland air
It's pudding and peas and a slice of bread please
Bolton's the one place for me

They can be unkind when they say we're behind
And we're still wearing cloth caps and clogs
We might still have backstreets but our houses are neat
It's not us who are going to the dogs
Our bitter is one of the best
It'll even mend holes in your vest
I'll make it quite clear I'm in love with the beer
Bolton's the one place for me

SID FAROUK

Emmanuel Shark was an agent
A sort of theatrical gent
He only booked oddballs and novelties
A sort of theatrical bent
He travelled the world for his artistes
What a collection he'd got
From them he scraped out a living
Just enough to buy his own yacht

In the Phillipines he found a show-stopper ...
A dancer with an eighty inch bust
She went down a rage, 'cause at night on the stage
She just crawled out and tried to stand up
But the star of his show came from Egypt -
Sid Farouk - from a long line of kings
For his performance at night he'd roger his twelve wives
And whoever was standing in t'wings

Tonight was the premiere performance
The theatre was full to the brim
Emmanuel sat tight, he'd been working all night
On ways to bring more people in
He'd doled out a fortune on adverts
But thought of the money he'd take
The posters said *'LOOK - Come & See SID FAROUK*
With His Wives & His One-Eyed Trouser Snake'

The rest of the cast was the usual
A sword swallower had the first job
Then a bloke juggling chimneys and cupboards and doors
And catching them all in his gob
A hypnotist next, but the crowd got quite vexed
For he spoke in peculiar lingo
There were cries from the back of *"Give him the sack"*
"Piss off home" and *"Ey up, when's the bingo?"*

When he'd taken his hook it was time for Farouk
No use having intervals and things
And from a very near riot the house went so quiet
That they heard a mouse fart in the wings
Sid Farouk came on stage with complete entourage
His wives, vaseline, and a bed
A gasp from the decks as he dropped down his kecks
And began what the posters had said

Before you could count three, or say *"Bugger me"*
He'd had six of his wives on the floor
Then he jumped on the bed where the rest of 'em laid
And proceeded upon the next four
The crowd went berserk as they saw him at work
Even Emmanuel was shouting for more
But when he came to the tenth poor Sid lost his length
Spun round and collapsed on the floor

The crowd didn't mutter, not a sigh did they utter
They thought it was part of the act
Though when he'd lain on the floor for ten minutes or more
They knew he wasn't acting, but whacked
With a mutter and groan people left to go home
Emmanuel sat there all sweating
He thought of the cost, all the money he'd lost
And the thumping from t'crowd he'd be getting

He jumped from his seat, leapt onto his feet
And rushed to the front in a rage
In one mighty fit he jumped clean over the pit
And stood next to Sid on the stage
He yelled *"What went wrong? Do a dance or a song"*
As he glanced at the crowd's mass dispersal
Sid opened one eye and replied with a sigh
"Dunno - it was all right at rehearsal"

Now all Egyptians have mummies, so it's perhaps not that funny
That an old lady appeared on the stage
By the way she jumped in on Emmanuel's chin
You could tell she was all of a rage
She said *"Time after time - it'll make you go blind"*
For she knew how he'd always made passes
Said Sid *"Well, today, I only got halfway*
So I might get away wearing glasses"

So beware then of hoaxers and all back-room boasters
Empty vessels make the most noise
And think on Farouk who, like King Canute
Thought he was one up from the rest of the boys
He recovered his strength and got back his length
With a diet of cucumber and mint
But to this very day, so Egyptians will say
He walks round with it still in a splint

HOLES IN THE ROAD

The water board and gasmen
There's a game that they both play
They take on all the council men
You can see them every day
They have no rules to work by
For they know no workers' code
They all see who can leave the biggest
Holes in the road

Near our house there lies a road
The subject of debate
They came to mend the water pipes
They were only three years late
They struggled on for four weeks
With no bonus, so I'm told
But they left some of the best and biggest
Holes in the road

Now some of these were large holes
And some of these were small
And in one the folks held concerts
'Bout the size of the Albert Hall
But one bloke filled the biggest hole
With water, so it's said
And ferried people into town
For 40p a head

The gasmen felt outdone by this
For they'd lose the holemakers' prize
So they disconnected the gas pipes
Blowing a hole of incredible size
Blaster Bates was envious at this feat
And so he told 'em
Put some dustbins down the hole
And call the place 'New Oldham'

When the 'leccy board heard of this feat
A terrible thing they did
They welded all their wires together
And fused the National Grid
The gasmen saw the hole they made
And trembled at the size
But they'd blown up all the roads they had
And no-one got the prize

The moral of this story's clear
As you have all been told
Thou shalt not covet thy neighbour's goods
And most of all, his holes
Or like the workers in this song
You'll wear a heavy load
They had no place to dig to leave their
Holes in the road

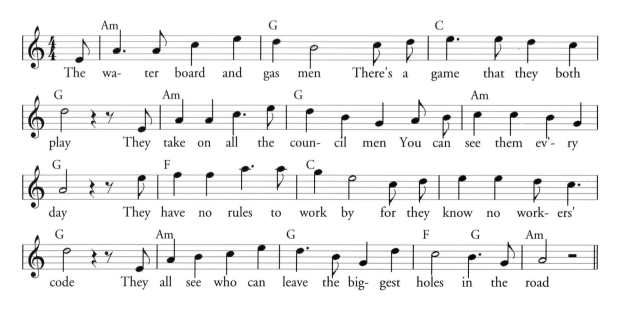

LANCASHIRE LASSES

I know a girl and she's called Annabella
She stands on our grid every night with a fella
And how do I know as her knickers are yella?
I go down our cellar for coal

My brother Bongo had a ten foot six dongo
His friends all remarked, saying how it was longo
But Bongo's long dongo is longer no longo
Since our Rover's got a new bone

CHORUS: I love them all, all the Lancashire lasses
The fat ones, the thin ones, the ones who wear glasses
The long ones, the short ones, the ones who make passes
It's Lancashire lasses for me

I once knew a fellow, by name Albert Dooley
Nature endowed him with different sized goolies
One of 'em was small and it looked rather poorly
But the other two were large and won prizes

The couple next door, whose name it is Kelly
Discovered one night they'd stuck belly to belly
They thought they'd been using petroleum jelly
But our Jimmy had swopped it for Bostik

CHORUS: I love them all, all the Lancashire lasses ...

My brother Billy, who works as a baker
In matters of sex is a little matchmaker
For he's just invented a dance called the Quaker
Once round then out for your oats

Our next door neighbour is called Mrs. Grover
She come to our door with a bone for our Rover
But Grover bent over, now Rover's in clover
For he slipped her a bone of his own

CHORUS: I love them all, all the Lancashire lasses ...

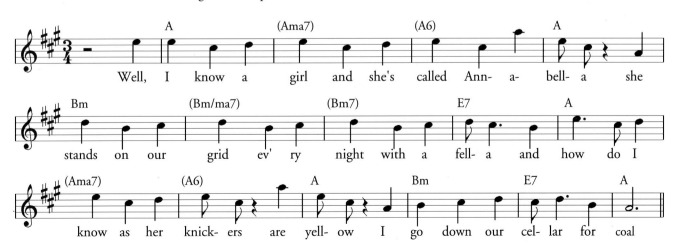

YOUNG MOLLY KERSHAW

I met a young lady last weekend
Her face looked familiar to me
I started to think on my past life
When it suddenly tumbled to me
I remembered that face from my childhood
The teaser from primary three
I see now you're dressed like a film star
But you'll still be young Molly to me

CHORUS: Don't put on an act, Molly Kershaw
No need for your nose in the air
No need for your airs and your graces
I know you from Jubilee Square

You used to be our ugly duckling
But now you look more like a queen
You know now which side your bread's buttered
I bet you don't use margarine
I remember a time, Molly Kershaw
When you were only a lass
Hopscotch and pig-in-the-middle
And we did things for fun, not for cash

CHORUS: Don't put on an act, Molly Kershaw ...

In Jubilee Square you are famous
Remembered by all of the cast
The good times you gave them still linger
Their heads turn as you're walking past
They say you're a director's mistress
Well, happen that's just as may be
But one thing I know, Lady Kershaw
You'll still be young Molly to me

CHORUS: Don't put on an act, Molly Kershaw ...

21

PLASTIC PIES

Standing on the station at a quarter past eleven
Hadn't had a bite to eat since I got up at seven
Then I espies a tray of tater pies
So I went up to the bloke and ordered four
I shot back to the table 'cause my stomach was quite sore
But as I did I slipped and dropped the first pie on the floor
It hit the deck and caught me on the neck
Then it bounced back to the plate just like before

CHORUS: Plastic pies are all I see and all I ever get
Plastic pies and rubber cakes'll polish me off yet
Well damn your eyes, and take your plastic pies
And you can shove 'em where the monkey shoves his nuts

I went back to the bloke and said *"This pie's as hard as hell"*
He looked the pie all over and said *"This one's not been well"*
He took off the crust and blew away the dust
Then said *"I'll change the oil and the points and plugs as well"*
I rushed back to the table where the first pie should have been
There were only crumbs upon the plate, and then I went quite green
It had crossed the floor, and walked out through the door
And it caught the half past twelve to Colwyn Bay

CHORUS: Plastic pies are all I see ...

An old man selling tortoises outside the pet shop door
A drunk came by and bought one then he come back for some more
He said *"Ey up Jack"* and clapped him on the back
And said *"I've never had pies as good as this before"*
Now prices they are rising fast 'cause no-one ever learns
And very soon we'll all see signs like 'Pies on Easy Terms'
90p a day would seem a lot to pay
When it's just for the deposit on the tray

CHORUS: Plastic pies are all I see and all I ever get
Plastic pies and rubber cakes'll polish me off yet
Well damn your eyes, and take your plastic pies
And you can shove 'em where the monkey shoves his nuts
That's up his arsehole
Shove 'em where the monkey shoves his nuts

22

CLOCKING WELL FED UP

Our factory isn't all that bad
Despite what people say
Though I could do with some more holidays
And a bit more take-home pay
The thing that really bugs me, though
What really turns me off
Is every morning clocking in
And evening clocking off

That clock upon the wall there
Is the thing I've grown to hate
It seems to smile an evil grin
And say *"Two minutes late"*
And when I shove the card in
I often wish instead
The card could be a hammer
And the clock the gaffer's head

It's a 1930s masterpiece
An ugly sort of clock
The glass is full of bootmarks
For it's shut with a seven inch lock
It never runs fast but I'll stake my life
They make the thing run slow
When I'm clocking off I can hear it say
"There's five more minutes to go"

This week I've clocked for Albert Smith
As well as for mysel'
Joe was on the ale last night
I'm clocking for him as well
And Harry from the house next door
Is off to sunny Spain
We all cast lots and muggins lost -
I'm clocking for him again

We have no clocks in our house
I gave them to our Jack
And as for the travelling alarm clock
It went out and never came back
But my mother, she can't take a hint
For when I was twenty-one
She gave me a special birthday treat -
A wrist watch for her son

Now I don't mind getting presents
Though I'd prefer a bottle of scotch
But how many blokes at twenty-one
Get a Hopalong Cassidy watch?
So I went and smashed her grandfather clock
My mum stood by and cried
It's not that she liked it all that much
But my grandad was still inside

Each time I go past Woolworth's
The town hall clock'll chime
And even putting the dustbin out
Someone asks *"Have you got the time?"*
My grandma left me a cuckoo clock
Bequeathed by her dying breath
But I never even touch it, me
I'm starving the cuckoo to death

Last night I had an awful dream
I dreamt I'd been retired
They were phasing out the working force
A computer had been hired
And as I shook the gaffer's hand
Like squeezing a sweaty sock
He said *"The lads have all chipped in
And bought you a nice gold clock"*

Seems to me it's out of hand -
The clock's become a curse
It rules us in the things we do
Instead of it being ruled by us
But thank you all for sitting still
To read this little rhyme
I would have written a bit more
But I haven't got the time

23

QUEENS OF THE HIGHWAY

I'll tell you of the Queens of the Highway
And believe me I'll tell you no flannel
It was told me first hand by the lads on the trucks
It's as true as I'm riding this camel

A clean girl is Nelly from Salford
She works around number nine dock
And she has a bath every Christmas
That's whether she needs one or not

And Gladys, the gobbler from Grantham
The Queen of the southbound A1
Had spent far too long on the trailers
And gave birth to a seven pot son

This little ten hundred by twenty
His face was a picture so glum
'Cause he'd E.R.F. stamped on his belly
And 3-4-REVERSE on his bum

One evening while strolling through Wigan
I bumped into a smart looking wench
Her knickers were down round her ankles
And her tights on a nearby bench

She was leant with her back to a building
Her skirt tucked up way past her hips
Her eyes held a moment of magic
Her hands held some fish, peas and chips

Well, I gave her the usual patter
I chatted the best that I could
When I asked her to look at my etchings
A voice from behind said he would

It was Jimmy, long distance from Glasgow
We both knew that he'd overheard
And he don't look too kindly on drivers
Who try to run off with his bird

He lifted his hand past his shoulder
He was built like the side of a bus
We heard a strange sound, it was then that I found
He'd bust the supports of his truss

'Twas this lack of support that had saved me
'Cause his whole body started to tilt
When he brought his arm down, well, he missed me
And he smacked himself right up the kilt

I didn't need encouraging further
I legged it clean out of the way
And I must have set up a few records
For there's scorchmarks on t'pavement today

So if I stay overnight on a long drive
I never move out of my digs
'Cause each time I hear a scotch accent
It moves me like syrup of figs

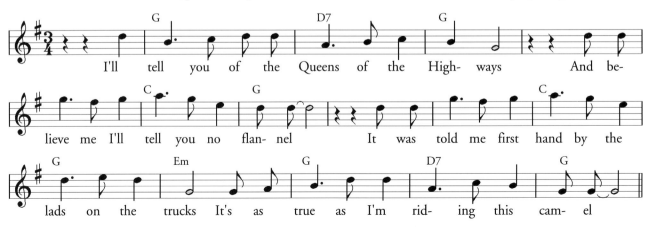

THE HALF TIMER

At five o'clock th'alf timer wakes, he's only just a lad
Then off to t'mill he'll go to learn a trade just like his dad
At first he'll fetch and carry things and maybe oil a cog
And if he dares to show his cheek, he'll feel the minder's clog

At dinner time he takes his bread and sits down on the stool
His head it nods but he daresn't sleep or he'll be late for school
Th'alf timer sits at t'back o t'class, his head cupped in his hands
His eyes they close and then he feels the back of teacher's hand

And so he's kept in after school to learn his ABC
A telling-off, some lines to write, then home to have some tea
A clout round th'ear for being late but t'lad he doesn't weep
'Cause all t'th'alf timer wants to do is go and have some sleep

And then he's off up wooden hill and in his prayers he'll say
"God bless the family and give me strength to face another day"
And through his sleep he'll happen dream of things to come, and when
Just as a gaffer he's become, it's five o'clock again

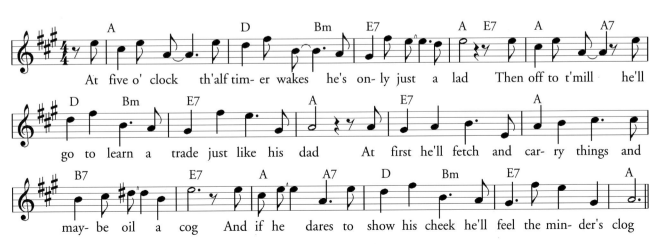

TRANSPORT DIGS

There's songs of transport drivers and about their fancy rigs
But you never hear a song about the famous transport digs
Yet they'll tell you tales of wagons passing everything in sight
And never give a mention of where they spend the night

Now there's good digs and there's bad digs and there's those that's in between
But why is it the bad ones are the only ones I've seen?
With twenty blokes in every room and three in every bed
And even little mouses have gas masks on their head

It's the digs, the digs, the transport digs
Where drivers spend the night
It's the digs, the digs, the transport digs
That made my hair turn white

It's bleedin' chips with everything, they're even round your cup
With plastic bread and butter, and tea you just daren't sup
The soup sticks to your insides, it turns the dishes brown
I've seen them use it afterwards to stick formica down

But thank God for the mustard, I use a pot a day
I spread it on as thick as I can to take the taste away
And when you work the cost out, it turns out rather cheap
'Cause you couldn't face another meal for at least another week

It's the digs, the digs, the transport digs
Where drivers rest their head
You can always tell the transport digs
There's tyre marks on the bed

When you've debugged all the bedclothes with the help of your left shoe
And you slide your six foot frame into a bed that's four feet two
With an army surplus blanket to keep the frost at bay
You shiver in your overalls until the break of day

At half past six it's breakfast time, you don't feel very bright
The meal they put before you is the one you left last night
Your eyeballs feel like sandpits, your mouth is full of fluff
But you're glad you stopped in these digs, 'cause some are really rough

It's the digs, the digs, the transport digs
Though some aren't very nice
It's the digs, the digs, the transport digs
They're cheap at twice the price

I play this in open Gm tuning - DGDGBbD - on the TEN TON SPECIAL album

ROBIN HOOD & THE BOGEY ROLLING CONTEST

In days of old when men were men
And all the sheep were nervous
There lived a bloke us poor folk like
'Cause he robbed the rich to serve us

He lived in the woods with a bunch of lads
He called his merry men
He called them that 'cause they drank so much ale
They got pissed eleven nights out of ten

There was Little John, who was not so small
In fact he was quite tall
If he had been small he'd have been called Big John
Which makes no sense at all

The fattest bloke in all the band
Was Tuck, the local friar
He kept his chip pan under his tunic
And two or three lads from the choir

Their minstrel they called Alan-a-Dale
They found him up at the friary
His mother kept record of the outlaws' deeds
In a book they called Mrs. a-Dale's diary

Will Scarlet was one for the ladies
It was short for 'willie' it's true
For he'd used it so much it went all red and pink
And his eyesight weren't up to much, too

There was also Much, the miller's son
Who always carried things on too far
You could tell what it was he'd indulged himself in
By the stains down the front of his bra

The Sheriff of Nottingham lived close by
And to him Robin was not partial
It was rumoured he couldn't stop picking his nose
So the King never made him a Marshal

One day, the Sheriff sat in his chambers
Musing on this and that
He'd picked his nose so heavily
He was through to the lining of his hat

He'd just got news of a robbery
On the day of his birthday, it seems
The outlaws had ambushed the guests to his party
And eaten all the Sheriff's ice cream

"Oh, hang those swine" the Sheriff cried
"If only somebody would"
Then he flicked a bogey at a passing fly
Which cured its headache for good

He swore *"For I'll trap the bold Robin Hood*
At a snot rolling contest, methinks"
But he didn't know Robin could roll Ten Ton Specials
And was a black belt at Tiddleywinks

When Robin got wind of the challenge
He thought *"Now there's trickery afoot"*
So he went down the Co-op to get ammunition
And came back with a bag full of soot

When they got off the bus at the castle
They realized they were in for a do
'Cause the Sheriff had filled his nose up with sawdust
And a tin full of Araldite too

He picked out a corker for starters
And gave Robin one on the neck
The weight of it made him stagger about
And laid him clean out on the deck

Then followed a barrage of bogeys
The sheriff sure knew how to shoot
Robin knew he had but one chance left
So he reached for his bag full of soot

He put his head in and breathed very deep
Then rolled a Ten Tonner for luck
He shaped it to be the first delta wing crow
So the Sheriff had no time to duck

The villain was floored, his plan had gone wrong
For it seemed now that Robin might win
So he picked as he never had picked before
But it was too much, and his head all caved in

Well, the outlaws hoisted Robin on their shoulders
They were so proud that he'd won the bet
And they stayed that way for the next fourteen days
'Cause the Araldite had started to set

They all went for a Chinese take-away
But they couldn't fit in, for a start
So they had to make do with the usual stew
While the friar tried to prise them apart

So there ends the story of bold Robin Hood
And of how he became England's best shot
There are some who still think his skill was with arrows
But, as I've just told you - it's not

FISHERMAN'S FRIEND

CHORUS: Go and have a suck on a Fisherman's Friend: Don't you dare stop till you get to the end
Take heed of this tip from the sons of the sea: If it's all right with sailors then it's all right with me

They give you a tingle from your head to your toes: They're safer than cocaine and won't rot your nose
They can cut a clear road through the densest of fog: And heal all the spots on a dalmation dog
CHORUS: Go and have a suck...

If they'd been around back in Beethoven's time: He'd have written more symphonies, & not stopped at nine
And what was behind all those wins by Red Rum: Why, the Fisherman's Friends that were stuck up his bum
CHORUS: Go and have a suck...

If you're into do-it-yourself they're a must: For they'll get rid of fungus and cobwebs and rust
As a laxative, they are the best one for miles: If you suck three at once they could melt down your piles
CHORUS: Go and have a suck...

COMMOTION IN THE CLUDGIE

If Owd Teddy Giles had gone in for a trophy
'Twould have been for the best boozer's cup
His wife could have gone for the fussbudget's medal
She spent all her time cleaning up

That day she's spring cleaning upstairs and down
When she thought to herself 'Silly moo'
For she'd run right out of the high powered stuff
That cleans round the bowl in the loo

You're always without when it's half day closing day
So Martha nipped into Ted's shed
Pinched some thinners where the lad kept his brushes
And poured the spirits down the lavvy instead

Just then the phone rang - it was Madge yet again
The local chief gossip and bore
So intent were the women that Martha never heard
Her Teddy come in the front door

He shot to the bathroom, scorch marks on the stairs
His afternoon hadn't been fun
He'd almost disgraced himself waiting for the bus
And had had to walk home, clenching his bum

At last he relaxed as he sat on the cludgie
And he laughed to himself at the joke
Then he fished out his matches, baccy and pipe
And proceeded to have him a smoke

He'd just put the still-lighted match down the bog -
When he thought that someone had shot him
With a blinding flash, a big bang and a crash
The world had dropped out of his bottom

He lay in the rubble, bent over double
With the toilet seat wrapped round his knees
Shouting *Martha, there's been a commotion in t' cludgie*
That's the last time we have mushy peas

The ambulance men got him stretchered
With his bum sticking up in the air
He told 'em what happened - they laughed till they shook
And they dropped Teddy right down the stairs

He made the front page of the paper
Which he read from his hospital bed
"MAN ATTEMPTS ORBIT FROM LAVATORY
GETS TWO COMPOUND FRACTURES INSTEAD"

So if you burn your bum just like Teddy
Take heed of this moral I beg
Don't tell t'paramedics how you did it
Coz they broke his arm and his leg

The neighbours still talk about Teddy
And some think they're being quite smart
When they think on that awful explosion
And say *Now that's what I call a fart*

BUGGERLUGS LOVES SUGARBUTTY

I'm your Buggerlugs, you're my Sugarbutty
When I'm in your hands you make me feel like putty
Ever since you met me on the tram
It's made me feel what a lucky Buggerlugs I am
My little Sugarbutty, tasty and neat
You are the bestest butty in our street
Say you're mine I'll love you all the time
BUGGERLUGS LOVES SUGARBUTTY

Only you could be so tender and sweet
Only you could have rushed me off my feet
And when we're alone and cuddling in the dark
I feel so good that my clog irons spark

I'm your Buggerlugs you're my Sugarbutty
We'll stick together like Sweep and Sooty
You be my sausage, I'll be your mash
When we've got each other who needs cash?
Since we met I don't have sugar in my tea
My little Sugarbutty is sweet enough for me
Our love will last 'cause we're both quite daft
BUGGERLUGS LOVES SUGARBUTTY

For one of your sweet kisses I'd run a mile
For one of your caresses I'd jump through a stile
But for what you gave me on the sofa last night
I'd polish a black pudding until it turns white

I'm your Buggerlugs you're my Sugarbutty
We'll stick together 'cause we're both quite nutty
When we get married and buy ourselves a house
We'll be closer than Mickey and Minnie Mouse
I'll put shelves up, you can make rugs
We'll have lots of little Buggerlugs
Say you're mine I'll love you all the time
BUGGERLUGS LOVES SUGARBUTTY

THE RETURN OF FARTING ARTHUR

The news got round, the word had spread, it would be a special day
Young Arthur Brown was coming back, for years he'd been away
They'd banished him for a dirty deed - some say it was a slip
For in church, before the sermon, our Arthur had let one rip

He said it was an accident - it could happen to me or you
But it wasn't the noise that put them off ... our Arthur had followed through
"We can't have this" the Lord Mayor cried - he almost blew his top
"Such dastardly deeds will be punished forthwith ... meantime, fetch us a mop"

They locked him in his bedroom and threw away the keys
His mother was pleaded for clemency - she blamed her last pie and peas
But they said he must be banished - a penalty rather stiff
The Gods weren't smiling on Arthur ... perhaps they'd had a whiff

Next day he caught the special train - his mother heaved a sigh
As the driver pooped upon his horn ... or was it Arthur saying goodbye?
He stayed away for seven years till at last the Mayor gave up
'Cause Arthur's mum had forged a note saying he'd had his bum stitched up

So Arthur returned to a civic do - the Mayor was doing them proud
The news of his return had spread, they were expecting quite a crowd
The townfolk waded into the grub, swilled down with hot teas and cold beers
"This pie and peas is lovely" said Arthur - *"I've not had this for about seven years"*

Mrs Brown was gobsmacked - she shouted *"Quickly, sound the alarm -*
It's the pie and peas" but the Mayor said *"He's cured - this note says he'll come to no harm"*
As he had spoke come the muffled roar of young Arthur suppressing a poop
The Mayor clenched his table in the first stage of shock - his glass eye looked up from his soup

Now time and tide wait for no man and neither for young Arthur Brown
For his first one had lifted the tablecloths off - his second brought the chandeliers down
The vicar had been lighting his pipe, and minding his business, he said
When a passing trump bubble ignited and blew his cassock right over his head

They struggled to get out the doorway - some drowned in the soup, others yelled
Then they saw a blur head through the exit... it was Arthur Brown - rocket propelled
The Mayor had ducked under the tables, uttering a trembling *"By gum"*
He'd been struck by the fixtures and fittings - then the turbo lag from Arthur's bum

They held an official enquiry and found 'subcontracting' was to blame
For the pie and peas had eventually come from the vets down Dogbollock Lane
So next time you're out at a function and they serve pie and peas as a must
Make sure that you check on the date stamp, located just under the crust
Or take a tip from his worship the mayor, who turned out to be not quite so dumb
He's made it a law now that all pie and peas must be served with a cork for your bum

THE MARTIANS HAVE LANDED IN WIGAN

There are strange goings on in a quaint Northern town
Which the folk there are trying to keep quiet
It'd cause a sensation but they're playing it down
For they're frightened of starting a riot
'Cause they've pit men with arms that are thirty feet long
And their heads are as smooth as boiled eggs
The man who sells pies has got three great big eyes
And the rugby league hooker is green with six legs

CHORUS: For the Martians have landed in Wigan
And they're wearing flat caps on their domes
And they've paid all their subs to the working men's clubs
'Cause Wigan reminds them of home

Now the Martians had lost all their bearings one night
'Cause the compass had gone up the spout
As they landed on t'slag heap the captain said, *"Right
We're home lads, so let's all pile out"*
Well they soon realised that they'd made a mistake
So some digs for the night they all booked
Where they'd trotters and hotpot and fresh Eccles cake
And when they tasted black puddings, those Martians were hooked

CHORUS: For the Martians have landed in Wigan...

Now the Martians play bingo and speak local lingo
Like, *"Sithee,"* and *"Ey up owd flower"*
From the pier every day you can go t'Milky Way
Or a UFO trip round Blackpool Tower
So next time you're passing through Wigan, look out
And remember the things I have said
Beware of the ones who have clogs on their feet
And aerials stuck out the tops of their heads

CHORUS: For the Martians have landed in Wigan...

There are strange go-ings on in a quaint North-ern town which the folk there are trying to keep quiet It 'd cause a sen-sation so they're play-ing it down 'cause they're fright-ened of start-ing a riot For there's pit-men with arms that are thir-ty foot long and their heads are as smooth as boiled eggs and the man who sells pies has got three great big eyes and the rug-by league hook-er is green with six legs For the Mart-ians have lan-ded in Wig-an and they're wear-ing flat caps on their domes and they've paid all their subs to the work-ing men's clubs 'cause Wig-an re-minds them of home

KING ARTHUR & THE CHASTITY BELT

King Arthur held his Guinevere right tenderly in his arms
Full well do I love thee, he spake to her ear, and all thy tender charms
But I must needs away for a while - the battle up North rages
And with this Awayday ticket I purchased I can take only my horse and two pages

"But soft" she cried; *"Don't call me soft"* said Arthur - *"I'm still the King*
And with my sword Excalibur I fight evil dragons and things"
"I didn't mean you" she said *"Oh, Arthur, you really are numb*
I merely meant, but stay a while" - said Arthur *"I can't - 'taxi's come"*

"Now while I trust your virtue as dearly as my own life
I trust not our Launcelot and his dastardly knights who forget that you are my wife
So you must wear this chastity belt, my own, my dearest prize
I've fixed a guillotine on the front - that'll cut philanderers right down to size"

So Guinevere was belted up, after Arthur had had one for the road
Then she packed up his butty bag with sarnies, and his flask with essence of toad
But as soon as she'd waved her noble king off, with crocodile tears in her eyes
She searched high and low for a suitable key to unlock the strange belt around her thighs

But try as she might she just couldn't budge the contraption strapped round her middle
Though the Knights of the Round Table were very obliging and they all queued up for a fiddle
At length she called Merlin to use his arc welder, for such was the strength of her passion
But after an hour the heat got too much and anyway, hot pants had gone out of fashion

And so it went on till one morning, just as the cock was crowing
She heard a commotion in the courtyard, and the sound of a trumpet blowing
"That sounds like Herb Alpert and his Tijuana brass - are they doing a concert right here?"
But there in the courtyard stood Arthur, returnèd, he was grinning from ear to ear

"I'm home, dear Guin, from the wars." he called, *"and our victory was quite a big 'un*
That'll stop those pie-eating wazzocks up North from wanting Home Rule for Wigan
And before I show you how strong and undying my passion for you has been
I must first check to see if those rampant knights have been faithful to King and Queen"

So he ordered his knights to assemble before him in front of the castle wall
And told them to drop their chainmail vests and their leather kecks and all
There was not one willy between them - their marriage prospects were wrecked
All except for Sir Launcelot who had everyting present and correct

"You perfidious bunch of black-hearted knaves, begone from these stately halls
When my back was turned you disgraced yourselves, so never more darken these walls
And well done, Sir Launcelot, trusty friend, you've proved all the rumours quite false
I dub thee Prime Minister, what say you now?". Said Launcelot *"?*?!?*?&%@$?!?"*

Well, it never struck Arthur that Launcelot, too, had been trying for his bit of fun
He thought the shock of the other knights' deeds had gone and struck him dumb
But the knights had the last laugh, and in a small way it made up for the pain that they felt
For that night, when Arthur was ravishing his Queen, he got cut short by her chastity belt

BREWER'S DROOP

Now here is a song that's directed
To all you young fellows who drink
You may think it's all right to get drunk every night
But this story should make you all think
For I've lifted so many beer glasses
My back is beginning to stoop
And what's even worse, I've fell prey to the curse
That's known as the dread Brewer's Droop

CHORUS: It's the Droop, the Droop, the dread Brewer's Droop
It's the cause of much dissatisfaction
It turns young men old and their sex life grows cold
'Cause they can't put their thoughts into action

I've sprayed it with starch and with lacquer
I've screamed and I've raged and blasphemed
And once, in a tantrum, I sang t'National Anthem
But it wouldn't stand up for the Queen
In desperation I tried levitation
To see if the bugger would rise
Though I've set it on fire it won't go no higher
It just brings the tears to my eyes

CHORUS: It's the Droop........

Last night I took off my trousers
And as I got into the bed
I could see the wife wearing black armbands
As a sign of respect for the dead
So you've heard my sad tale, and it's over
How my love life's been blighted by booze
Once I was proud it reached up to my hat
But now it just points at my shoes

CHORUS: It's the Droop........

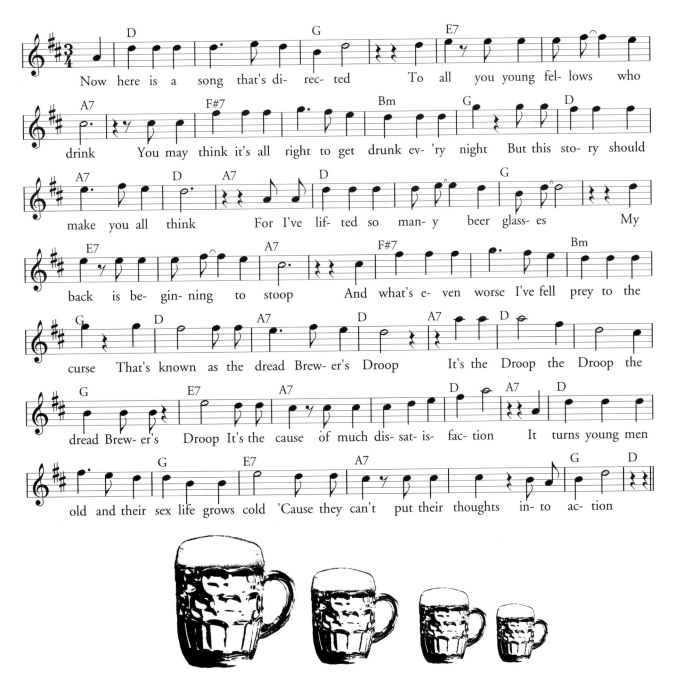

Now here is a song that's di- rec- ted To all you young fel- lows who

drink You may think it's all right to get drunk ev- 'ry night But this sto- ry should

make you all think For I've lif- ted so man- y beer glass- es My

back is be- gin- ning to stoop And what's e- ven worse I've fell prey to the

curse That's known as the dread Brew- er's Droop It's the Droop the Droop the

dread Brew- er's Droop It's the cause of much dis- sat- is- fac- tion It turns young men

old and their sex life grows cold 'Cause they can't put their thoughts in- to ac- tion

WHEN GRANNY SANG ME SONGS

There's a shoebox in the attic full of fading photographs
Which we take out when the rain clouds fill the sky
Then we spread the pictures on the rug and an hour or two we pass
And we see the way things were in years gone by
For fashions change and people change but memories stay the same
And they stay with you whatever comes along
And the photographs remind me of the good old-fashioned days
When I was young and granny sang me songs

CHORUS: Now the kids have television
And they've pockets full of cash
They don't go short of anything but love
And though I'm just old-fashioned,
I don't know the rights or wrongs
But I'd rather be back in the days
When granny sang me songs

Now granny used to tell me of the days when she was small
When times were hard but people always smiled
And how, when times got better, no-one smiled at all
And I listened with the wonder of a child
And when I think about her I remember happy times
When granny smiled and stroked my sleepy head
And how she'd sing me special songs and funny little rhymes
And, contented, I would toddle off to bed

CHORUS: Now the kids have television....

Well, kids today tread different ways and sing a different song
They've other things to keep them occupied
And no-one seems to listen, the world goes crashing on
No-one looks for pictures in the fire
So talk to one another, and remember granny's ways
For she can show you where your heart belongs
And though she's gone, the pictures keep alive those distant days
When I was young and granny sang me songs

CHORUS: Now the kids have television....

VASECTOMY

Albert was a quiet lad, he liked a quiet life
He hadn't any kids, but he'd a domineering wife
One day she said, *"I've had enough, so if you love me still*
The contraception's up to you, I'm going off the pill"
"Whatever can I do," he thought, *"Don't I get all the luck*
I can't start using condoms - they choke the neighbour's duck
I'll have to think of something else, another remedy
There's only one course open - and that's vasectomy"

CHORUS: Oh, dear, Albert, whatever have you done
You'll never have a daughter, you'll never have a son
I hope the doctor told you you're on a one-way trip
There is no way to change your mind when the scissors have gone SNIP

He went to his physician to ask for his advice
He said *"Have the operation, they'll do it in a trice*
The waiting list is fifteen years on the National Health
But slip me fifty guineas and I'll do the job myself"
He gave the man the money, had the job done right away
Then walked home like a cowboy whose horse had gone astray
He couldn't stand, he couldn't sit, 'twas agony to cough
And when he held his breath it felt like things were falling off

CHORUS: Oh, dear, Albert, ...

His conjugal equipment turned a funny shade of green
What used to be his pride and joy was nowhere to be seen
He said, *"There's been a cock-up, the surgeon's gone too far*
I bet it's on his desk now, inside a pickling jar"
A week went by and things got worse, he was bruised and feeling sore
He counted up his assets and found that he'd got four
He'd one like a marble next to a pointed one
And one shaped like a tennis ball, with a tennis racquet on

CHORUS: Oh, dear, A1bert, ...

He has a deep affection now for tomcats and the like
It's put him right off eating chips and he never rides his bike
He won't go near the cobblers, he comes out in a rash
And if he sees a doctor, he could win a ten mile dash
So if you've got some money, old fashioned lsd
And you want a way to spend it, then try vasectomy
You may find that you like it, you could have yourself a ball
Or two or three or even four, or maybe none at all

CHORUS: Oh, dear, Albert........

BACK IN THE OLD SCHOOLYARD

Cast your mind back in time to days when you were small
Happy times, nursery rhymes and playmates I recall
Ring o' ring o' roses, handstands by the wall
Back in the old schoolyard
Chasing girls with golden curls to play at Kiss Me Quick
Run to the man in the ice cream van, lollies we would lick
Jubblies and Bubblies, quite often we were sick
Back in the old schoolyard

CHORUS: Back in the old schoolyard, Back in the old schoolyard
Seems so long ago we were happy there I know
Back in the old schoolyard

May have been small but I recall then everything seemed big
Thrashing round that old playground with endless games of tig
The baddest word you ever heard was to call someone a pig
Back in the old schoolyard
Whenever I was monitor the milk was always late
I remember well that awful smell of bottles in the crate
Outside bogs, full of dogs, but at times you couldn't wait
Back in the old schoolyard

CHORUS:

Ran like hell when we heard the bell and had to hide our toys
Weather fine we'd stand in line, the girls and then the boys
Woe betide if anyone tried to move or make a noise
Back in the old schoolyard
We'd drive the teacher daft collecting frogspawn in a jar
Sit in the sun, stick your thumb in bubbles made of tar
Songs we sang till the schoolbell rang still haunt me from afar
Back in the old schoolyard

CHORUS:

SATURDAY COWBOYS

Half past nine on a Saturday morning, birds are singing, dogs are yawning
There's a great excitement in the air
Down along each cobbled street, there comes the sound of tiny feet
The games have stopped, no time to stand and stare
Sixpences they're clutching tightly, little eyes all shining brightly
Happy laughing kids without a care
As they skip and dance along, they start to sing a special song
And Saturday Cowboys sing it everywhere

CHORUS: They're singing ... Mister, mister, why are we waiting
Saturday Cowboys don't like waiting
Come on down and give them doors a push
We want to see Lassie and Rin-Tin-Tin
And Charlie Chaplin makes us grin
Saturday Cowboys love the Saturday Rush

Saturday Cowboys rush to the pictures, clutching lollies and dolly mixtures
We'll all get there faster if we run
I've stuck my six-gun down my sock, the usherette's in for a nasty shock
When a plastic bullet hits her up the bum
Doors fly open, in they tumble, through the dark they feel and fumble
Every cowboy's got his favourite seat
Then they hear the manager shout, *"Oi! Make less noise or I'll chuck you out"*
And they don't want to miss their Saturday treat

CHORUS: They're singing ... Mister, mister ....

Smoking woodies and striking matches, cheering t'cavalry, booing t'Apaches
See Roy Rogers shoot that baddie dead
I've told my mum that when I'm bigger, I'll buy a horse that's just like Trigger
And fill that pesky rent man full of lead
Suddenly, the lights go on - the show is over, the West is won
No more tomato ketchup to be shed
Twelve o'clock on a Saturday morning, birds still singing, dogs still yawning
Saturday cowboys' eyes are tired and red

last CHORUS: They're singing ... Mister, mister, why are we waiting
Saturday Cowboys don't like waiting
Dinner's ready, so give them doors a push
Hi-yo Silver, away we go
Galloping down the road-e-o
Saturday Cowboys have been to the Saturday Rush

WHO PUT THE THING IN THINGIE?

For thirteen years I went to school, to learn my ABC
Not to mention art and maths and trigonometry
They showed us all the weather maps from here to Timbuktu
But still there are some questions no-one knows the answers to

Who put the arse in parsley, who put the birk in Birkenhead
Who put the wind in Swindon, Aunty Mary says it wasn't Uncle Fred
Who put the pis in pistol, who put the dung in dungarees
Who put the biz in business, if you know won't you tell me please

I went to ask Miss Jobson, way back in the infant school
She told me I was a silly girl and must not play the fool
Then when I reached the juniors, I asked old Mr. Crowe
But all he did was cane me - I suspect he didn't know....

Who put the fart in farthing, who put the riddle in Bridlington
Who made the pong in ping-pong, well if he knew then he wouldn't let on
Who put the dong in ding-dong, who put the turd in Saturday
Who put the willy in Williamson - it could have been his brother, he's funny that way

When I went to grammar school, I asked a teacher there
He took me gently by the neck and lightly by the hair
He bounced me up and down and then I felt thc end of his shoe
But I think it was a cover-up, because he never knew

Who put the gin in virgin, who put the liver in Liverpool
Who put the crap in scrapping, I wish I knew 'cause I feel a fool
Who put the wank in swanking, who put the tit in titillate
Who put the 'oles in rissoles, oh, tell me please 'cause I just can't wait

Last week I found a crumpled note shoved underneath my door
It said, "My name's A. Nonymous, the bloke you're looking for
Now, all these words are naughty ones, I'm sure you will agree
So I've hidden them in bigger words so people cannot see

And I put the bum in album, I put the clit in Clitheroe
I put the prick in prickly, I did it so no-one would ever know
And I put the poo in poodle, I put the dic in dictaphone
Yes I put the orp in Scunthorpe, and now you know you can bugger off home

BLACK PUD STUD

CHORUS: I'm the Black Pud Stud from Bolton I like 'em big and round
I've got a tasty handful for the girls all over town
I don't know what goes in 'em but I eat 'em by the pound
I'm the Black Pud Stud and I'll do you good
'Cause you can't keep a good man down

Now every night when I go to bed I get down on my knees
And I thank the Lord for all his gifts like pies and mushy peas
But the thing that packs a wallop, 'cause it does your love life good
Is a great big steaming, fat and juicy plateful of black pud

CHORUS: I,I, I'm the Black Pud Stud from Bolton.......

Well, Popeye had his spinach, Desperate Dan liked cow pie best
But I stuff myself with black pud till I'm bulging out my vest
I never eat cream crackers, I don't like fish and chips
I like to feel the black pud juice a-dripping down my lips

CHORUS: I,I, I'm the Black Pud Stud from Bolton....

So be careful of black puddings, they move in mysterious ways
Don't take them on your honeymoon they'll set the sheets ablaze
Our barmaid said she wouldn't, and then she said she would
But then she wished she hadn't 'cause she's in the pudding club

CHORUS: I,I, I'm the Black Pud Stud from Bolton....

I- I- I'm the Black Pud Stud from Bol- ton I like 'em big and round I've
got a tas- ty hand ful for the girls all ov- er town I don't know what goes in 'em but I
eat 'em by the pound I'm the Black Pud Stud & I'll do you good coz you can't keep a good man
down Now ev- 'ry night when I go to bed I get down on my knees & I
thank the Lord for all his gifts like pies & mush-y peas But the thing what packs a wal-lop coz it
does your love life good is a great big steam- ing fat & jui- cy plate- ful of black pud

Bernard Wrigley cassettes and CDs are available to view and order at his website, just point your browser towards **www.bernardwrigley.com**

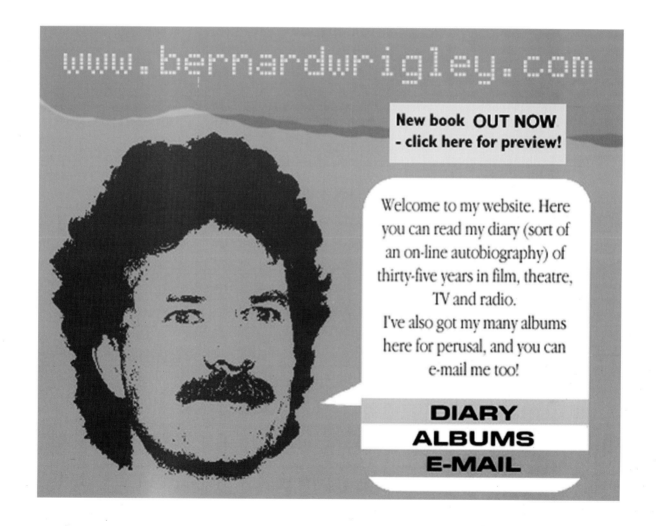